Popular Songs for the
CLASSICAL GUITAR

Arranged by John Zaradin.

Wise Publications
London/New York/Sydney/Paris/Copenhagen/Madrid/Tokyo

Exclusive distributors:
Music Sales Limited
8/9 Frith Street, London W1V 5TZ, England.
Music Sales Pty Limited
120 Rothschild Avenue, Rosebery, NSW 2018, Australia.

Order No.AM963941
ISBN 0-7119-8159-0
This book © Copyright 2000 by Wise Publications.

Book design by Michael Bell Design.
Compiled by Mick Barker.

Photograph courtesy of Redferns.

Printed in the United Kingdom by Printwise (Haverhill) Limited, Haverhill, Suffolk.

Your Guarantee of Quality:
As publishers, we strive to produce every book to the
highest commercial standards.
The book has been carefully designed to minimise
awkward page turns and to make playing from it a real pleasure.
Particular care has been given to specifying acid-free, neutral-sized paper
made from pulps which have not been elemental chlorine bleached.
This pulp is from farmed sustainable forests and
was produced with special regard for the environment.
Throughout, the printing and binding have been planned to ensure
a sturdy, attractive publication which should give years of enjoyment.
If your copy fails to meet our high standards,
please inform us and we will gladly replace it.

Music Sales' complete catalogue describes thousands
of titles and is available in full colour sections by subject,
direct from Music Sales Limited.
Please state your areas of interest and send a
cheque/postal order for £1.50 for postage to: Music Sales Limited,
Newmarket Road, Bury St. Edmunds, Suffolk IP33 3YB.

www.musicsales.com

ALL MY LOVING
Words and Music: John Lennon and Paul McCartney.

Play in tempo and with 'bounce'.

THE FIRST TIME EVER I SAW YOUR FACE
Words and Music: Ewan MacColl.

AND I LOVE HER
Words and Music: John Lennon and Paul McCartney.

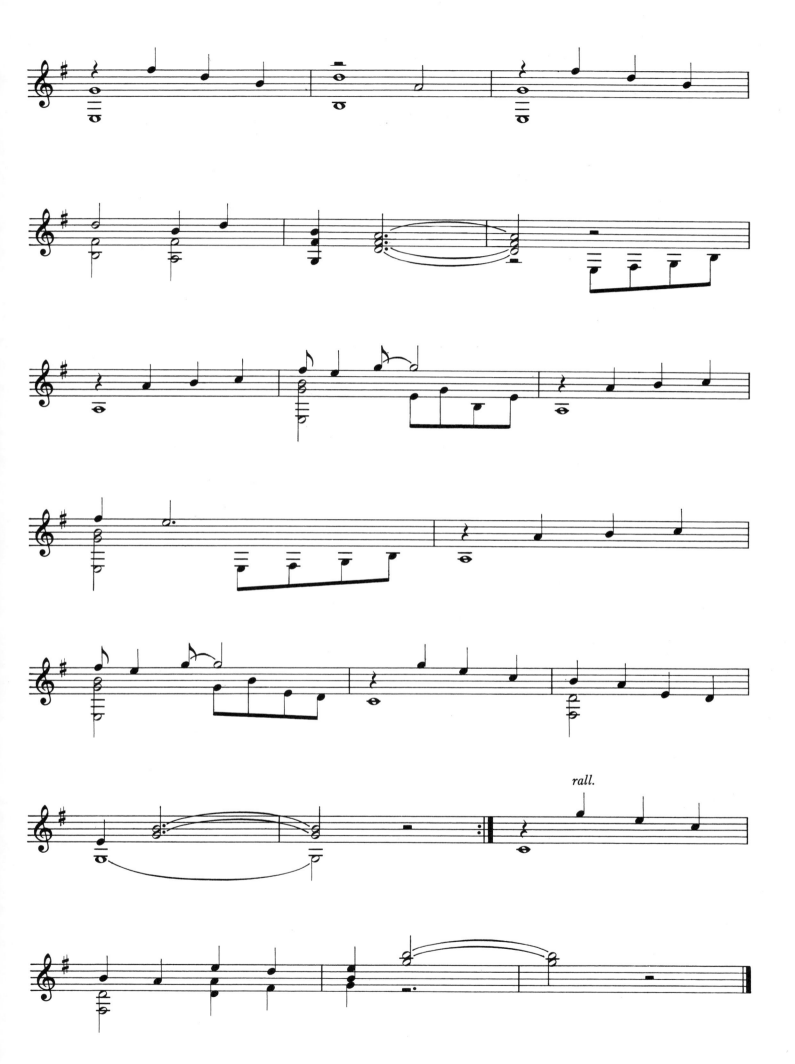

THE SOUND OF SILENCE
Words and Music: Paul Simon.

MIDNIGHT IN MOSCOW
Based on a song by Vassili Soloviev and M. Matusovosky
New musical arrangement by Kenny Ball.

FALLING IN LOVE AGAIN
Music and Original Words: Friedrich Hollander
English Words: Reg Connelly.

Dreamily, Chopinesque.

HAWAII FIVE-O
By: Mort Stevens.

PETITE FLEUR (Little Flower)
Words and Music: Sydney Bechet.

Sustain melody on long notes.

MICHELLE
Words and Music: John Lennon and Paul McCartney.

KILLING ME SOFTLY WITH HIS SONG

Words: Norman Gimbel
Music: Charles Fox.

YESTERDAY
Words and Music: John Lennon and Paul McCartney.

IT'S A RAGGY WALTZ
Music: Dave Brubeck.

Play with a very rhythmic feel, jazz 3 feel.

SUNNY
Words and Music: Bobby Hebb.

CHARADE

Words: Johnny Mercer
Music: Henry Mancini.

Play with a tight jazz waltz feel.

ELEANOR RIGBY
Words and Music: John Lennon and Paul McCartney.

Play the introduction broadly and then attack the theme in strict tempo.

SATIN DOLL
Words: Johnny Mercer
Music: Duke Ellington and Billy Strayhorn.

Make sure that the bass creates momentum from the beginning.
Play with a restrained 'held back' feel.

A NIGHT IN TUNISIA

Music: Frank Paparelli and John Dizzie Gillespie
Words: Raymond Leveen.

Set the mood as 'Latin' with the introduction. I have written a bridge fill
at the end of the first chorus before returning to theme,
but I would encourage each player to invent his own.

To Coda ✦

D.%. al Coda

CODA

LOVER MAN (Oh Where Can You Be)

Words and Music: Jimmy Davis, Roger Ram Ramirez and Jimmy Sherman.

This is a real 'jazz classic' with some dramatic bluesy chord changes.

TAKE FIVE
By: Paul Desmond.

Play the 5 beats as 3 + 2. I have written a short section in the style
of an improvisation before returning to the melody.
However, feel free to add your own variations.

LULLABY OF BIRDLAND

Music: George Shearing
Words: George David Weiss.

Play this with definite drive and swing.